# Little RIDDLERS

## Derbyshire & Nottinghamshire

Edited By Jenni Harrison

First published in Great Britain in 2018 by:

YoungWriters

Young Writers
Remus House
Coltsfoot Drive
Peterborough
PE2 9BF
Telephone: 01733 890066
Website: www.youngwriters.co.uk


Book Design by Ashley Janson

SB ISBN 978-1-78896-592-7
Printed and bound in the UK by BookPrintingUK
Website: www.bookprintinguk.com
YB0361NZ

# FOREWORD

Dear Reader,

Are you ready to get your thinking caps on to puzzle your way through this wonderful collection?

Young Writers' Little Riddlers competition set out to encourage young writers to create their own riddles. Their answers could be whatever or whoever their imaginations desired; from people to places, animals to objects, food to seasons. Riddles are a great way to further the children's use of poetic expression, including onomatopoeia and similes, as well as encourage them to 'think outside the box' by providing clues without giving the answer away immediately.

All of us here at Young Writers believe in the importance of inspiring young children to produce creative writing, including poetry, and we feel that seeing their own riddles in print will keep that creative spirit burning brightly and proudly.

We hope you enjoy riddling your way through this book as much as we enjoyed reading all the entries.

# CONTENTS

## St George's Primary School, Church Gresley

| | |
|---|---|
| Isobel Sadie Gwilliam (6) | 136 |
| Isabelle Adams (6) | 137 |
| Zachary Davies (6) | 138 |
| Maisy Autumn Brooks (6) | 139 |
| Sebastian Whiten (6) | 140 |
| Matthew Ball (6) | 141 |
| Ruqayya Alexandra (6) | 142 |
| Oscar Edwards (6) | 143 |
| Nayeli Isaacs (7) | 144 |
| Oscar James Clamp (7) | 145 |
| Evie Davies (6) | 146 |
| Holly Forrest (7) | 147 |
| Emily Davis (7) | 148 |
| George Elwyn Weighall (6) | 149 |
| Olivia Sophia Cook (6) | 150 |
| Phoebe Leah Felthouse (7) | 151 |
| Leila Miles (6) | 152 |
| Maisie Bailey (6) | 153 |
| Jessica Morritt (6) | 154 |
| Tallula Young (7) | 155 |
| Chloe Warrilow (7) | 156 |
| Skye Cuthbert (6) | 157 |
| Chelsey Jerome (6) | 158 |
| Oliver-Jack Grime (7) | 159 |
| Tianna Gutteridge (7) | 160 |
| Makayla Avah Foster (6) | 161 |

## Stanley St Andrew's CE Primary School, Stanley

| | |
|---|---|
| Molly Marianne Rowan (6) | 162 |
| Elizabeth Knifton (7) | 163 |
| Amelia Lister (6) | 164 |
| Elliot Sullivan (7) | 165 |
| Oliver Crowder (6) | 166 |
| Edie Kate Hughes (6) | 167 |
| George Izzard (7) | 168 |
| Lily Deley (6) | 169 |
| Joseph Harry Smyth (7) | 170 |
| Lochlan Campbell (6) | 171 |
| Aimee Dennis (7) | 172 |
| Fearne Hilditch (7) | 173 |
| Jack Stephenson (7) | 174 |
| Kayden Brent Hodson (7) | 175 |
| Olivia Bradley (6) | 176 |
| Dalacey Peace (6) | 177 |
| Logan Doughty (7) | 178 |
| Imogen Izzard (7) | 179 |
| Lucas Pierrepont (6) | 180 |
| Olivia Grace Dennis (7) | 181 |

# THE POEMS

# What Am I?

I am blue, white and green
I look like a big, round ball
You can't see me, I live up in the sky
You can't touch me
I go around the sun
I am small, tiny
My home is dark
You can't come to my house
What am I?

Answer: Earth.

**Siobhan Irene Speakman (6)**
Combs Infant School, Chapel-En-Le-Frith

# Can You Guess What I Am?

I am round
I am the same colour as myself
I am juicy
I have dimples
I have a little seed inside me
I grow
It is hard to peel me
I am soft
You can eat me
What am I?

Answer: An orange.

**Lewis D G M Marshall (6)**
Combs Infant School, Chapel-En-Le-Frith

# Can You Guess?

I like warm water
I can be lots of colours
I live in the sea
People buy me
I am very nice
I am an animal
I am not dead
I breathe under the water
What am I?

*Answer: A tropical fish.*

**Sienna Longden (7)**
Combs Infant School, Chapel-En-Le-Frith

# Guess What?

I'm fast
I have lots of energy
I am crazy, I love walks
I am spotty
I'm cute
I wag my tail
I'm fluffy
I love hugs
I'm funny
What am I?

*Answer: Jack Russell.*

**Dolly Rose Burford (7)**
Combs Infant School, Chapel-En-Le-Frith

# Who Am I?

I have four legs
I make people laugh
I'm very naughty
I bark at who passes by
People call me 'Long Tongue'
I drop hairs everywhere
Who am I?

Answer: Daphne (dog).

**Sorrel Hutchins (6)**
Combs Infant School, Chapel-En-Le-Frith

# Mystery

I have a big beard
I deliver presents around the world
I have eight reindeer
I have mini helpers
I have a big sleigh
I visit you every year
Who am I?

*Answer: Santa Claus.*

**Max Daniel Oxbury (5)**
Combs Infant School, Chapel-En-Le-Frith

# Can You Guess?

I am fluffy
I purr when you stroke me
I walk in people's houses
My owners feed me
I hunt for mice
I go out of a flap in the door
What am I?

Answer: A cat.

**Ben May (6)**
Combs Infant School, Chapel-En-Le-Frith

# Guess What I Am?

I can bounce
I can climb
I am at a football match
I like to be outside
I can go into a tree
You can fit me in the shed
What am I?

*Answer: A football.*

**Scarlett Ebony Ellis (6)**
Combs Infant School, Chapel-En-Le-Frith

# Can You Guess What I Am?

I run fast
I have spots
I live in Africa
I have four legs
I can't swim
I am the fastest in the world
What am I?

Answer: A cheetah.

**Eddie Chapman (5)**
Combs Infant School, Chapel-En-Le-Frith

# What Am I?

I have four legs
I'm not an animal
I am sometimes comfy
People sit on me
You can find me in buildings
What am I?

Answer: A chair.

**Lochlainn Douglas-Mullett (5)**
Combs Infant School, Chapel-En-Le-Frith

# Figure It Out

I have land
I have water
I float in space
I'm green and blue
People live on me
I'm a circle
What am I?

Answer: Earth.

**Lewis Hall (5)**
Combs Infant School, Chapel-En-Le-Frith

# What Am I?

I have white and black fur
I can jump because I have strong legs
I can jump on the sofa
I climb trees and I hide in them
I lie on the sofa so I get some sleep
What am I?

Answer: A kitten.

**Samuel Donald Roberts Cope (7)**
Copthorne Community Infant School, Alfreton

# What Am I?

I have grey skin and big feet
I can make loud noises
I make loud noises when I move
I live in a dark, warm jungle
I eat lovely brown and green leaves
What am I?

Answer: An elephant.

**Max Williams (7)**
Copthorne Community Infant School, Alfreton

# What Am I?

I have a fierce face and scary teeth
I can eat meat and flesh
I make a howling sound
because I want to be scary
I like to eat juicy flesh
What am I?

Answer: A wolf.

**Finley Harris (7)**
Copthorne Community Infant School, Alfreton

# What Am I?

I have black spots
I can leap and run fast!
I have yellow fur
I don't have sharp teeth
I have a short tail so I don't trip
What am I?

Answer: A leopard.

**Ryan Buckley (6)**
Copthorne Community Infant School, Alfreton

# What Am I?

I have green, thin skin
I can dive deep down underwater
And I can *ribbit* loudly
I have great, big eyes
I have short legs
What am I?

*Answer: A frog.*

**Riley Humphreys (7)**
Copthorne Community Infant School, Alfreton

# What Am I?

I have grey or black fur
I can eat meat
I make a loud noise like *hawoo*
I am scary and fierce and have sharp teeth
What am I?

Answer: A wolf.

**Rhys Taylor (7)**
Copthorne Community Infant School, Alfreton

# What Am I?

I have a brown body and I can do tricks
I can play fetch and I have got four legs
I have got four legs and brown fur
What am I?

*Answer: A lion.*

**Oliver Castledine (6)**
Copthorne Community Infant School, Alfreton

# What Am I?

I have grey skin
I can make noises with my trunk
I go to sleep sometimes
You can see me at the zoo
What am I?

Answer: An elephant.

## Joshua Martin (6)

Copthorne Community Infant School, Alfreton

# What Am I?

I have green skin
I make a croak
I can jump so high and I can leap
I sleep on four legs
What am I?

*Answer: A frog.*

**Layton Ley Wake (7)**
Copthorne Community Infant School, Alfreton

# What Am I?

I am fast
I am yellow
I have a lot of hair on my face
I can roar
I am a big cat
What am I?

*Answer: A lion.*

**Alex Lopez (6)**
Copthorne Community Infant School, Alfreton

# What Am I?

I have a fluffy belly
I can run very fast
I love people
I make a barking noise
What am I?

*Answer: A dog.*

**Lacie Liston-Taylor (7)**
Copthorne Community Infant School, Alfreton

# What Am I?

I have stripes
I can run so fast
I am black and white
I look like a horse
What am I?

Answer: A zebra.

**Kaleb Ryn (7)**
Copthorne Community Infant School, Alfreton

# What Am I?

I have stripes on my back
I can hunt for birds
I can roar very loud
What am I?

Answer: A tiger.

**Jayden Robert Moore (7)**
Copthorne Community Infant School, Alfreton

# The Beautiful Flower

I look like a heart of love
I'm a symbol of love
You can find me in the shop
I'm special because of love
I am red like blood
I make every event beautiful
On your birthday you like to see me
What am I?

Answer: A red rose.

**Bakhita Zeb (6)**
Fig Tree Primary School, Hyson Green

# The Cover

I look like a sheet of paper
that is folded in half
I live in a red, shiny pillar box
You communicate instead of calling
on a telephone
On your birthday you love to see me
What am I?

Answer: An envelope.

**Syeda Hafsa Anwar (7)**
Fig Tree Primary School, Hyson Green

# What Am I?

I look like a small tiger
I sound like a cute baby
You find me in your house
I have four legs and cute eyes
I have a black and white body
I feel soft and fluffy
What am I?

Answer: A cat.

**Faqeha Shahbaz (5)**
Fig Tree Primary School, Hyson Green

# What Am I?

I look as fluffy as a rug
I sound like a squeaky door
You find me in your house
I am cute and pretty
I feel very soft and fluffy
What am I?

Answer: A cat.

**Fatima Akmal (6)**
Fig Tree Primary School, Hyson Green

# What Am I?

I look like a tall tree
I sound like a squeaky toy
You find me at the lush tree
I have a tall neck
I am yellow and brown
What am I?

Answer: A giraffe.

**Shaista Sadaf (8)**
Fig Tree Primary School, Hyson Green

# What Am I?

I look like a tall building
I sound like a plane
You find me in the zoo
I am yellow and brown
I feel very tall
What am I?

Answer: A giraffe.

**Aina Khan (6)**
Fig Tree Primary School, Hyson Green

# What Am I?

I look like a little hand
I sound like a squeaky toy
You find me in your house
I am very cute
I feel very safe
What am I?

Answer: A mouse.

**Muhammad Hisham Hafeez**
Fig Tree Primary School, Hyson Green

# What Am I?

I look like a zebra
I sound like a lion
I live in the jungle
I am orange and black
I feel like a soft teddy
What am I?

Answer: A tiger.

**Mohammed Adam Hussain (6)**
Fig Tree Primary School, Hyson Green

# What Am I?

I live in damp, freezing, cold weather
with some other animals.
I like to soar through the sky,
look down quickly at all the animals.
I eat grass, leaves, long, sweet leaves,
and fresh, freezing cold water.
My skin is very, very, very fluffy
but my beak is as strong as sharp nails.
When you touch, I might bite your finger.
What am I?

Answer: A parrot.

**Evie Taylor (6)**
Firfield Primary School, Breaston

# What Am I?

I have big brown spots,
yellow fur and four long legs.
My neck is as long as a wavy tree.
I live in the green and juicy grassland.
I love to eat the green, crispy,
wet leaves and grass.
I don't like meat because I'm a herbivore.
I move slowly and steadily
through the trees.
What am I?

*Answer: A giraffe.*

**Evie Mcgugan (6)**
Firfield Primary School, Breaston

# What Am I?

I have stripes on my back.
I am very tall and I look out for danger.
My fur is as yellow as sand
and my head is very small.
I live in the hot, steamy desert.
I love to eat scorpions and ants.
I don't like grass because I am a carnivore.
I move round tree stumps quickly.
What am I?

Answer: A meerkat.

**Charlotte Ellis (6)**
Firfield Primary School, Breaston

# What Am I?

I have orange fur and hair
all around my neck and head.
My food is meat as hard as rock.
I live in the swishy grass.
I love to eat my prey,
my food is other animals.
I move on four legs and I don't like walking,
I like running.
I kill other animals in the wild.
What am I?

Answer: A lion.

**Joel George Franklin (6)**
Firfield Primary School, Breaston

# What Am I?

I have a big body, big ears and small tail.
My head is as big as lots of tree branches.
I live in deserts, grasslands and caves.
I like to eat long grass,
drink water and eat flowers.
I don't like tree branches
because they are wood.
I move by stomping loudly.
What am I?

Answer: An elephant.

**Grace Patricia Fennemore (7)**
Firfield Primary School, Breaston

# What Am I?

I have tiny feet, small legs
and I'm peach coloured.
My tail is as short as a mouse's tail.
I live in the sandy and dusty Kalawi desert.
I like to eat red and juicy scorpions.
I don't like snakes because they eat me.
I move as slowly as a tortoise.
What am I?

Answer: A meerkat.

**Lexie Mason (6)**
Firfield Primary School, Breaston

# What Am I?

I live in the boiling, steamy savannah.
I live in the tall, yellow grass.
I like going fighting for a girlfriend.
I eat small grassy leaves.
I eat long, green grass.
When I eat I make the leaves rustle.
When I walk I make the grass crunch
and rustle.
What am I?

*Answer: A giraffe.*

**Yasmin Blocker (6)**
Firfield Primary School, Breaston

# What Am I?

I have white, sharp and pointy teeth.
I move quite slow but not too slow.
My eyes are as black as night.
I live in the green grasslands.
I don't like leaves because I'm a carnivore
not a herbivore.
I love to eat hard, crispy and crunchy bones.
What am I?

Answer: A hyena.

**Violet Warwick (6)**
Firfield Primary School, Breaston

# What Am I?

I have sharp, small, white,
pointy and triangular teeth.
My body is as long as a giraffe's neck.
I live in shallow rivers.
I love to eat juicy meat.
I don't like crispy plants
because I am a carnivore.
I move as slow as a slug.
What am I?

Answer: A crocodile.

**Charlie Thomas Hunn (7)**
Firfield Primary School, Breaston

# What Am I?

I live in a wet, damp, grassy forest.
I like to jump and pounce.
I like to eat big, fat, juicy chops of animals.
I have spotty, yellow skin.
When I am cross I make a noise like *roaaar!*
When I am happy I make a noise like *eee!*
What am I?

Answer: *A jaguar.*

**Ed (7)**

Firfield Primary School, Breaston

# What Am I?

I live in the huge, wild, roaming jungle.
I like to lie down in the summer sun.
I eat anything that moves,
or I will squash it to death.
My skin is scaly and slimy,
and my body is filled with patterns.
I make a hissing and a sssing sound.
What am I?

Answer: A snake.

**Elizabeth Scullard (6)**
Firfield Primary School, Breaston

# What Am I?

I have pointy ears, spots and long legs.
My neck is as tall as a tree.
I live in the sandy, steamy and hot desert.
I love to eat green, juicy and crispy leaves.
I don't like meat because I'm a herbivore.
I move slowly and steady.
What am I?

*Answer: A giraffe.*

**Molly Price (6)**
Firfield Primary School, Breaston

# What Am I?

I have a tall, long neck.
I have a long, fluffy tail.
I have long legs.
I move slowly, steady and carefully
through the trees and the savannah.
I love getting crunchy leaves
that are dark and bright green.
I eat a lot of food.
What am I?

*Answer: A giraffe.*

**Darci Nolan (6)**
Firfield Primary School, Breaston

# What Am I?

I have big, gigantic and enormous ears.
My trunk is as long as rope.
I live in the long, green grasslands.
I like to eat crispy, fresh grass and leaves.
I don't like meat because I am a herbivore.
I move with big stomping.
What am I?

Answer: An elephant.

**Elodie Flanagan (7)**
Firfield Primary School, Breaston

# What Am I?

I live in the long grass, the grass is sharp.
I live on the grasslands of Africa.
I like to walk very slow
apart from when a predator is chasing me.
I don't make a sound but I am still big.
My fur is bright, some of my fur is dark.
What am I?

*Answer: A giraffe.*

**Abi Emily Smith (6)**
Firfield Primary School, Breaston

# What Am I?

I live in the steamy, hot grassland
and in the deep, dark jungle.
I like to go on the tall trees.
I like to eat anything I see
and I squeeze it to death.
I have strong skin like a reptile.
I am so quiet that you can't hear me.
What am I?

Answer: A snake.

**Harvey Glover (6)**
Firfield Primary School, Breaston

# What Am I?

I have black and white stripes.
I sometimes fight with other animals.
I live in the rainforest.
I love to run about
and I like eating crunchy leaves.
I don't like meat because I am a herbivore.
I move steadily and slow.
What am I?

Answer: A zebra.

**Riley East (7)**
Firfield Primary School, Breaston

# What Am I?

I have a scaly, windy body
and a red tongue.
My teeth are as sharp as a needle.
I live in the deep, dark jungle.
I love to eat red, juicy meat.
I don't like plants because I'm a carnivore.
I move slowly like a slug.
What am I?

Answer: A snake.

**Benjamin Carr (7)**
Firfield Primary School, Breaston

# What Am I?

I have a tall neck, tall, tall legs
and a long, long belly.
My neck is as long as a tree.
I live in the hot, steamy savannah.
I love to eat green and crispy leaves.
I don't like meat because I'm a herbivore.
What am I?

Answer: A giraffe.

**Lucia Maria Morris (6)**
Firfield Primary School, Breaston

# What Am I?

I have a hairy mane,
bright fur and wild eyes.
My claws are as sharp as a knife!
I live in a dark, cold cave.
I love to eat big, juicy meat.
I don't like plants because I'm a carnivore.
I move slowly and fast.
What am I?

*Answer: A lion.*

**Anna Cartwright (6)**
Firfield Primary School, Breaston

# What Am I?

I have a big body
with a big trunk and long legs.
My ears are round as a ball.
I live in the hot savannah.
I love to eat the big, long grass.
I don't like running because I am so big.
I move slowly and steady.
What am I?

*Answer: An elephant*

**Isla Cammack (7)**
Firfield Primary School, Breaston

# What Am I?

I live in the tall, spiky grasslands.
I eat other animals like zebras
and hunt with style.
I have fat legs and thick fur.
I like to hunt my prey and eat my juicy meat.
When I'm grumpy I growl
and call the others.
What am I?

*Answer: A lion.*

**George Richardson (6)**
Firfield Primary School, Breaston

# What Am I?

I live in the deep, dark forest with my family.
I like to climb the tallest trees in Africa
and sleep there.
I eat juicy meat joints.
My skin is brown and yellow.
When I prey on you,
you will not hear me creep.
What am I?

Answer: A leopard.

**Daisy Iris Hopkinson (7)**
Firfield Primary School, Breaston

# What Am I?

I have long, sharp and scary claws.
My body is as little as a mouse.
I live in the hot, steamy desert.
I love to eat scorpions, ants and beetles.
I like to eat meat because I'm a carnivore.
I move very fast!
What am I?

Answer: A meerkat.

**Chloe Rose (7)**
Firfield Primary School, Breaston

# What Am I?

I live in the long, wavy grass.
I like to creep up on animals.
I eat fresh, juicy meat,
my favourite food is zebra.
My skin on my body is yellow
and a different part of me is orange.
I move fast and silently.
What am I?

*Answer: A lion.*

**Alma Lindley Philimore (6)**
Firfield Primary School, Breaston

# What Am I?

I live in a steamy, hot savannah,
with tall, spiky grass.
I like leaves and weeds.
I eat weeds, leaves and grass.
I have grey skin.
I don't like other animals to come near me.
I don't make a noise.
What am I?

Answer: A rhino.

**Freya White (7)**
Firfield Primary School, Breaston

# What Am I?

I live in the steamy, spiky grass.
I like spitting poison at other animals.
I eat little, juicy baby chicks and mammals.
My skin is smooth and slimy,
but I have no fur and no legs.
My sound sounds like a hiss.
What am I?

Answer: A python.

**Romello Squire (6)**
Firfield Primary School, Breaston

# What Am I?

I have grey, shiny, sharp claws.
My claws are as sharp as a needle.
I live in the hot, sandy desert.
I love to eat red, juicy meat.
I don't like leaves because I am a carnivore.
I move slowly and fast.
What am I?

Answer: A cheetah.

**Callan Crawshaw (7)**
Firfield Primary School, Breaston

# What Am I?

I live in a dark, spooky cave.
I like to hunt and hide in the grass.
I eat big animals
to have lots of energy to run fast.
My skin is dark and light.
I move like a leopard
and I hide in the large grass.
What am I?

*Answer: A lion.*

**Chloe Mia Rumble (6)**
Firfield Primary School, Breaston

# What Am I?

I live in the burning, hot savannah.
I like to pounce
on the big and small animals.
I like to eat other animals' sweet meat.
My skin feels furry.
When I'm hurt, I make a dog's crying sound.
What am I?

Answer: A hyena.

**Finley Hughes (7)**
Firfield Primary School, Breaston

# What Am I?

I have a furry mane,
terrifying teeth and a long tail.
My mane is as furry as my body.
I like to eat red, juicy meat.
I don't like grass because I am a carnivore.
I move as fast as a cheetah.
What am I?

*Answer: A lion.*

**Eva Grace Denny-Szadura (6)**
Firfield Primary School, Breaston

# What Am I?

I live on a dark black rock in the sand.
I like to hide in the yellow sand.
I like to eat blue, shiny beetles.
I have black, hard skin.
I sound like a loud click.
I am a very small animal.
What am I?

Answer: A scorpion.

**Mikey Espinoza (6)**
Firfield Primary School, Breaston

# What Am I?

I have a long neck, and small spots.
My spots are as dark as night.
I live in the hot, steamy savannah.
I love to eat long leaves off the trees.
I don't like meat because I am a herbivore.
What am I?

Answer: A giraffe.

**Olivia Grace Godsall (7)**
Firfield Primary School, Breaston

# What Am I?

I live in the boiling, scorching, savannah.
I like lazing and fast hunting.
I eat sweet, squashy meat.
My skin is spotty.
I laugh and laugh and laugh.
When something happens, I laugh.
What am I?

Answer: A hyena.

**Mia Helen Storer (7)**
Firfield Primary School, Breaston

# What Am I?

I live in the silky grasslands.
I like to chase other juicy, soft animals.
I eat fluffy, juicy meerkats.
My skin has thick skin with brown spots.
When I'm angry, I growl and rumble,
What am I?

Answer: A cheetah.

**Yasmin Thwaites (7)**
Firfield Primary School, Breaston

# What Am I?

I have black spots.
I am yellow and I have four legs.
My teeth are as sharp as knives!
I live in a big, hot desert.
I love to eat juicy meat.
I don't like big, juicy plants.
What am I?

Answer: A leopard.

**Sam Shadam (7)**
Firfield Primary School, Breaston

# What Am I?

I have a small and round body.
I am as slithery as a slug.
I live in the hot green grassland.
I love to eat crunchy leaves.
I don't like to eat meat
because I am a herbivore.
What am I?

Answer: A snake.

**Matthew Butcher (7)**
Firfield Primary School, Breaston

# What Am I?

I live in the tall, spiky grass.
I like to creep up on other animals.
I like to eat zebras and wildebeest.
My skin is orange brown.
When I creep up I don't make a sound!
What am I?

*Answer: A lion.*

**Sophie Amelia Brown (6)**
Firfield Primary School, Breaston

# What Am I?

I live in the fiery, hot savannah.
I like to creep really, really slowly.
I have yellowy fur.
I eat juicy meat.
I make a bellowing roar.
I sneak really, really slowly.
What am I?

Answer: A lion.

**Emmie Gibson (6)**
Firfield Primary School, Breaston

# What Am I?

I live in the steamy hot savannah
and the spiky grass.
I like to eat other animals.
I have yellow skin on my head
as well as lots of hair on it.
I roar so loud.
What am I?

Answer: A lion.

**Charlie Towle (6)**
Firfield Primary School, Breaston

# What Am I?

I live in the hot, steamy, savannah.
I like to eat and nibble leaves.
I eat spiky, juicy leaves.
My legs are long and thin.
My neck is about two metres long.
What am I?

Answer: A giraffe.

**Verity Warwick (7)**
Firfield Primary School, Breaston

# What Am I?

I live in a boiling, hot grassland.
I like fresh and yummy meat.
I have thin, soft fur.
I eat delicious meat
and yummy, fresh gazelles.
My skin is yellow.
What am I?

*Answer: A lion.*

**Ellie James (6)**
Firfield Primary School, Breaston

# What Am I?

I live in the long, grassy, steamy, grasslands.
I like to swish my tail to get the flies away.
I like to eat fresh, juicy leaves.
I have white and black skin.
What am I?

Answer: A zebra.

**Isla Sophie Roseveare (7)**
Firfield Primary School, Breaston

# What Am I?

I have a big body and pointy ears
and sharp nails.
My neck is not as tall as a tree.
I live in the wild.
I love to eat meat.
I move so very fast.
What am I?

*Answer: A lion.*

**William Hutchinson (6)**
Firfield Primary School, Breaston

# What Am I?

I live near trees and high grass fields.
I like to hunt slowly then quickly.
I move fast like a train.
I have fur like a sheep.
What am I?

*Answer: A lion.*

**Beau Skinner (6)**
Firfield Primary School, Breaston

# Bugs

I'm faster than a snail
And I have a fluffy tail
I don't wear bows
But I have a twitchy nose
I have long whiskers
And despite what you may think
I do not hibernate in winter
I am not a mole
But I live in a hole
I have short legs
And I deliver eggs
My babies are called kittens
But none of them have lost my mittens
What am I?

*Answer: A rabbit.*

**Ingrid Esau (7)**
Halam CE Primary School, Halam

# Under The Sea

I'm actually an animal
but look like a little tree
I'm found with lots of fish
in the warm, blue sea
Hard on the outside but soft within
All shapes and sizes, spiky, smooth or thin
I can be any colour of the rainbow,
bluer than the sky
Do you think you can guess?
What am I?

Answer: A coral.

**Lily Zara Smith (8)**
Halam CE Primary School, Halam

# Mystical Weather

I am full of colour
Some think I keep gold
where my feet touch the ground
You can see me but can't touch me
When you move closer to me
I move further away
When the sun and the rain meet together
I show up in the weather
Some people think unicorns dance under
me
What am I?

Answer: A rainbow.

**Summer Sanchez (7)**
Halam CE Primary School, Halam

# Chip Scavenger

I have a razor-sharp beak
Chips and fish is what I seek
I'm not very picky about what I eat
I live mostly at beaches and cities too
Watch out for me
when I'm zooming across the sky
I'll be swooping and swirling until I feel dizzy
What am I?

Answer: A seagull.

**Beatrice Marsden (6)**
Halam CE Primary School, Halam

# Double Trouble

Two furry friends
Both love miaowing for food and a stroke
Both mischievous, climbing Mum's curtains
swinging side to side
Sitting on my homework but I don't mind
I love them so much
They climb on the bath side to kiss me
What are they?

Answer: Kittens.

**Ben Adlington (7)**
Halam CE Primary School, Halam

# Whiskers

I am small and furry
With eyes that shine at night
I have sharp claws
And I like to hunt mice at night
I like to snuggle on my owner's lap
I purr when you stroke me
I have whiskers
If you talk to me I will miaow back
What am I?

Answer: A cat.

**Sophia Elisabeth Whitaker (6)**
Halam CE Primary School, Halam

# Mountain Wanderer

I am black and white
I roam mountain ranges
I am nearly extinct
I am a type of bear
I eat bamboo
I am most likely to be found in China
I can be found in captivity
When I am born I am pink, blind,
and toothless
What am I?

Answer: A panda.

**Florence Basten (8)**
Halam CE Primary School, Halam

# Blind Blower

I have a fat face sometimes
I have a tail
I have four toes at the front
I make a squeak if I'm scared
I am blind
I'm a great pet
I'm very small
I can go through small spaces
What am I?

Answer: A hamster.

**Kate Grace Drury (7)**
Halam CE Primary School, Halam

# My Cuddly Friend

She hops everywhere she goes
She has a very twitchy nose
Her ears are furry and long
She doesn't join in when I sing her a song
She lives in a big cosy hutch
And is so cute, I love her very much
What is she?

Answer: A rabbit.

**Annabel Boyles (6)**
Halam CE Primary School, Halam

# Cuddly

I am enormous and white
I'm so fluffy I look like a teddy bear
You'll think I'm very cuddly
I walk on a white blanket
I catch fish for a living
I'm fierce inside
What am I?

Answer: A polar bear.

## Darcey Bond (7)

Halam CE Primary School, Halam

# Rainbow Of Colour

I have a horn,
I might be pink and fluffy,
There is a song about me,
I might be big or small,
I might even be white,
I have a fluffy tail,
I have four legs,
What am I?

*Answer: A pink, fluffy unicorn.*

**Emma Key (7)**
Halam CE Primary School, Halam

# Brum

A lot of mums and dads have me
You get me in different types and colours
I am made in different countries
I need cleaning
I can get you places quickly
Some people make me
What am I?

Answer: A car.

**Harry Bex (7)**
Halam CE Primary School, Halam

# The Amazing Case

I always need a key!
I have very valuable jewels inside
I am wooden and hard
I might have a golden lock
Some people must have unlocked me
And I might be heavy
What am I?

Answer: A treasure chest.

**Rocco Vincenzo Freeborn (8)**
Halam CE Primary School, Halam

# Easter Animal

I am fluffy and soft
I like to eat carrots
I live in a burrow
I have a white bobtail
I have long ears and a twitchy nose
You might see me at Easter time
What am I?

Answer: A rabbit.

**Annabelle Tyler (6)**
Halam CE Primary School, Halam

# A Jungle Life

Swinging through the jungle trees
I like to eat bananas
I look like you except I have a tail
I am furry
I am silly and cheeky
I am from Africa
What am I?

Answer: A monkey.

**Charlie Stowe (8)**
Halam CE Primary School, Halam

# A Purr-Fect Pet

I am scared of dogs
I hunt for lots of fish
I can be ginger
I like to go to sleep in the sun
I can see in the dark
I have a tail and whiskers
What am I?

Answer: A cat.

**Eddie Wright (6)**
Halam CE Primary School, Halam

# Playful

I am very cute
I like to sit on your lap
I like to be stroked
I like to play with wool
I am small and furry
I like to cuddle
What am I?

Answer: A kitten.

**Poppy Boud (7)**
Halam CE Primary School, Halam

# A Secret Animal!

I have big, fluffy ears
I am cute and cuddly
I live in Australia
I have brown eyes
I climb eucalyptus trees
I have paws
What am I?

Answer: A koala bear.

**Bethan Fogarty (7)**
Halam CE Primary School, Halam

# Melody Maker

I have keys
I can be small or grand
I have hammers
I have sharps and flats
I have two pedals
A lovely sound comes from me
What am I?

*Answer: A piano.*

**James Colella (7)**
Halam CE Primary School, Halam

# Delicious

I am round with bread on the top
and meat in the middle
I am sometimes friends with chips
Cheese and lettuce sit with me
What am I?

Answer: A hamburger.

**Henry Davies (6)**
Halam CE Primary School, Halam

# Mystical Creature

I am beautiful and magical
I am a little bit furry
I have wings
I fly
I love gummy bears
I have rainbow poo
What am I?

Answer: A unicorn.

**Kyla Priestley (7)**
Halam CE Primary School, Halam

# Half-Cat, Half-Unicorn

I shoot out rainbows
I am half cat half unicorn
I am grey
I am cute
I run fast
I have a horn
What am I?

Answer: A unicorn Pusheen.

**Freya Brace (7)**
Halam CE Primary School, Halam

# Out In The Night

I am a nocturnal animal
I perch on branches
I have large eyes
I come in different types
I hunt my prey
What am I?

Answer: An owl.

**Henry Ian (7)**
Halam CE Primary School, Halam

# Spiky Ball

I am spiky and brown
I can climb
I eat delicious bugs
I don't like winter so I hibernate
What am I?

Answer: A hedgehog.

**Elijah Sanchez (5)**
Halam CE Primary School, Halam

# Damp Weather

I am very helpful
I am used for wet things
People use me
I keep you dry
I get wet
What am I?

Answer: An umbrella.

**Israeli Abigail Shaw (7)**
Halam CE Primary School, Halam

# Cute

I am black and white and furry
I have a long tail
I like walks and delicious bones
What am I?

Answer: A dog.

**Brooke Bond (5)**
Halam CE Primary School, Halam

# A Leaping Lord

I am green with black spots
and I live in a pond
I am slimy
I have long legs
What am I?

*Answer: A frog*

**India Hayes (6)**
Halam CE Primary School, Halam

# Funny

I am funny and I make people laugh
I have a colourful wig
I do lots of tricks
What am I?

Answer: A clown.

**Jack Christopher Patrick Bevans (6)**
Halam CE Primary School, Halam

# A Place To Live

I have windows and doors
People make me look nice
I keep people warm and safe
What am I?

Answer: A house.

**Thomas Carney (6)**
Halam CE Primary School, Halam

# Skit Me

I am purple and cream
I have a lovely voice
I am shy and cute
I am small
Who am I?

*Answer: Skitty.*

**Lana Jelley (8)**
Halam CE Primary School, Halam

# Fluffy

I am big and fluffy
I am soft and white
I make shapes as I float in the sky
What am I?

*Answer: A cloud.*

**Eleanor Stowe (5)**
Halam CE Primary School, Halam

# Just Like Me

I have arms and legs
You play with me
You can dress me and give me a name
What am I?

Answer: A doll.

**Ava Atherley (5)**
Halam CE Primary School, Halam

# Pretty

I have a sparkly horn and fluffy wings
I am pretty and cute
I fly in the sky
What am I?

Answer: A unicorn.

**Rachel Key (5)**
Halam CE Primary School, Halam

# Shiny

I am round and yellow
I live in the sky
I make people hot and happy
What am I?

Answer: The sun.

**Mia Laura Anne Woods (5)**
Halam CE Primary School, Halam

# Magical

I have wings and a pointy horn
I have four legs
I like to fly
What am I?

Answer: A unicorn.

**Lily Greenwood (5)**
Halam CE Primary School, Halam

# Humpty

I am big and strong
I'm tall and brown
I have humps
What am I?

Answer: A camel.

**Alexa Priestley (5)**
Halam CE Primary School, Halam

# King Kong

I have hairy arms
I move loudly and grumpily
I eat green, bright leaves
I live in a hot jungle with bright leaves
I am as loud as Tarzan
I can swing from tree to tree
What am I?

*Answer: A gorilla.*

**Rosie Fagan (6)**
Hallcroft Infant & Nursery School, Retford

# Elsa

I have silky, soft fur
I move quickly and I canter
I eat juicy grass and crunchy apples
I live in magical fairy land
I neigh like a horse
I have four legs
What am I?

Answer: An alacorn.

**Alicia Hewitt (7)**
Hallcroft Infant & Nursery School, Retford

# What Am I?

I have a gold horn
I move fast and I trot
I eat hay, grass, carrots and apples
I live in a forest
I neigh just like a horse
I work in a circus
What am I?

Answer: A unicorn.

**Grace Turner (6)**
Hallcroft Infant & Nursery School, Retford

# Sharpy

I have scaly and slippery skin
I move quickly and sneakily
I eat fish
I live in the deep, dark ocean
I squeak like a dolphin
I have a sharp fin
What am I?

Answer: A shark.

**Autumn Brooke Nevard (7)**
Hallcroft Infant & Nursery School, Retford

# Glitter

I have orange, fluffy fur
I move quietly and slowly
I eat chickens and rabbits
I live under a droopy tree
I yap like a dog
I have orange ears
What am I?

Answer: A fox.

**Iris Lola Upson (6)**
Hallcroft Infant & Nursery School, Retford

# The Jungle

I have black and orange, stripy fur
I can run very fast
I eat other animals
I live in a hot country
I growl like a lion
I am a big cat
What am I?

Answer: A tiger.

**Owen Hodson (6)**
Hallcroft Infant & Nursery School, Retford

# The Chomper

I have grey, scaly skin
I move fast and I glide
I eat crunchy fish
I live in the blue sea
I chatter like a dolphin
I can swim
What am I?

*Answer: A shark.*

**Raymond Brown (6)**
Hallcroft Infant & Nursery School, Retford

# Goldy

My skin is gold
I move slowly
I eat grass
I live in the garden
I sound like a snake
I live in a warm environment
What am I?

Answer: A beetle bug.

**Matthew Shaw (7)**
Hallcroft Infant & Nursery School, Retford

# Silver Tooth

I have soft, woolly fur
I can run very fast
I eat out of a bowl
I live in a den
I grunt like a bull
I have a wet nose
What am I?

Answer: A dog.

**Ollie Spence (6)**
Hallcroft Infant & Nursery School, Retford

# Benny

I have furry skin
I move really fast
I eat a little bit of nut
I live in a house
I nibble on my food
I have four feet
Who am I?

Answer: Benny.

**Isabelle Parkinson (7)**
Hallcroft Infant & Nursery School, Retford

# Speed

I have lots of spots
I glide quickly
I kill rabbits
I live in a busy forest
I roar fiercely
I have sharp teeth
What am I?

Answer: A cheetah.

**Riley James Thorpe (6)**
Hallcroft Infant & Nursery School, Retford

# Bite

I have thick skin
I move fast and speedy
I eat fish
I live in the ocean
I bite like a lion
I can't walk
What am I?

Answer: A shark.

**Tumas Benas Zakarauskas (7)**
Hallcroft Infant & Nursery School, Retford

# Charlie

I have sharp claws
I move fast
I eat grass
I live in a house
*Woof!*
I snap when you get in my face
What am I?

Answer: A dog.

**Caden Noble (7)**
Hallcroft Infant & Nursery School, Retford

# Chester Brown

I have brown fur
I can run fast
I eat food from a bowl
I live in a house
I bark a lot
I am a pet
What am I?

Answer: A dog.

**Will Noble (6)**
Hallcroft Infant & Nursery School, Retford

# Cutey

I have soft brown fur
I move fast
I eat meat
I live in an animal house
I bark
I am cute
What am I?

Answer: A puppy.

**Ava Dainty (6)**
Hallcroft Infant & Nursery School, Retford

# Mr Hiss

I have shiny scales
I slither quietly
I eat rats
I live in Africa
I hiss
I can bite you
What am I?

Answer: A snake.

**Scott M Bowen (6)**
Hallcroft Infant & Nursery School, Retford

# Chester

I eat meat
I have black spots
I have sharp teeth
I bark loud
I run fast
I wiggle my tail
What am I?

Answer: A dog.

**Edward Parkinson (7)**
Hallcroft Infant & Nursery School, Retford

# What Am I?

I have green and black spikes
I move really slowly
I snap up rabbits!
I snap my sharp teeth
What am I?

Answer: A crocodile.

**Ayden John Cooper (7)**
Hallcroft Infant & Nursery School, Retford

# Jaws

I have smooth skin
I move quickly
I eat fish
I live in the ocean
I chatter like a dolphin
What am I?

*Answer: A shark.*

**Roxi Fagan (6)**
Hallcroft Infant & Nursery School, Retford

# Pinkie Love

I am furry
I move slow
I eat grass
I live in a field
I neigh loudly
I am nice
What am I?

Answer: A pony.

**Abbie Allcock (6)**
Hallcroft Infant & Nursery School, Retford

# Chester

I have fluffy skin
I move fast
I bite a bone
I live in a house
I woof loudly
What am I?

*Answer: A dog*

**Zac Noble (6)**
Hallcroft Infant & Nursery School, Retford

# Flower

I have fluff
I have a sharp horn
I move and canter
I live on a hill
What am I?

Answer: A unicorn

**Scarlet Davies (6)**
Hallcroft Infant & Nursery School, Retford

# Stompy

It has huge round ears
It can sometimes be found in Africa
It squirts water wildly at its feet
It eats leaves off green, bushy trees
It likes to walk around
with her enormous, stampy feet
It can sometimes be found in a zoo
It is a big animal so likes to eat lots of food
It squirts water out of her trunk
What is it?

Answer: An elephant.

**Isobel Sadie Gwilliam (6)**
St George's Primary School, Church Gresley

# Long Neck

It is a mammal
It has brown little spots on its neck
It has two small brown hoops on its head
It has a tail, yellow neck and spots
It has some brown patterns
It has four legs
It has a long neck
so it can reach tasty leaves off trees
It is clever at munching leaves off trees
What is it?

*Answer: A giraffe.*

**Isabelle Adams (6)**
St George's Primary School, Church Gresley

# Scale

It has deadly, fearsome claws
Its piggish, snappy mouth eats birds,
fish and humans
It carries its babies in its mouth
It lives on both land and water
It has a long, bumpy tail
It has scaly, rough skin
It has furious, emerald eyes
It has a spiky, green back
What is it?

*Answer: A crocodile.*

**Zachary Davies (6)**
St George's Primary School, Church Gresley

# Swimmer

It can swim in water
It lives in the freezing cold
It has a pointy, orange beak
It has some swishy black wings
It is a bird but it can't fly
It has lots of warm feathers
It lives in the southern hemisphere
It has orange webbed feet
What is it?

*Answer: A penguin.*

**Maisy Autumn Brooks (6)**
St George's Primary School, Church Gresley

# Spotty

It flies everywhere gracefully
It has black, big spots
It's a bug you find in the spring and summer
It lives on land
It is smooth and small
It has white eyes and a black face
It lives anywhere on land
It's ruby, red and black
What is it?

Answer: A ladybug.

**Sebastian Whiten (6)**
St George's Primary School, Church Gresley

# Slithery

It has a long, ruby tongue
It slithers around quickly
It has red, vicious eyes
It has a huge, colourful tail
It is a reptile
It lives in the jungle
It has no legs
It is a carnivore
It is a deadly, frightening creature
What is it?

Answer: A snake.

**Matthew Ball (6)**
St George's Primary School, Church Gresley

# The Grey Animals

It has a grey, humungous trunk
It has gigantic, round ears
It eats tall grass and has long, bushy trees
It has huge, white toes
It drinks deep, cold water
It lives in a big herd
It has four legs
It has big, pink ears
What is it?

Answer: An elephant.

**Ruqayya Alexandra (6)**
St George's Primary School, Church Gresley

# Swinging

It swings weirdly in the trees
It likes to eat yellow, brilliant bananas
It is a marvellous animal
It lives in the zoo and forests
It has a brown body
It has round ears
It is quite small
It has circular hands and feet
What is it?

Answer: A monkey.

**Oscar Edwards (6)**
St George's Primary School, Church Gresley

# Jumping Carrots

It has a round, fluffy tail
It hops quickly around the garden
It eats leaves, plants and carrots
It has two long ears
It is little and it has two fierce teeth
It doesn't like water
It has small eyes
It is soft
What is it?

Answer: A rabbit.

**Nayeli Isaacs (7)**
St George's Primary School, Church Gresley

# Roary

It has a monstrous, loud roar
It has sharp claws
It lives in a pride with other animals
It has a red, spiky mane
It is a strong, rough animal
It is a carnivore because it eats zebras
It is dangerous
It is not nice
What is it?

*Answer: A lion.*

**Oscar James Clamp (7)**
St George's Primary School, Church Gresley

# Stompy

It is a huge grey mammal
It has a gigantic, light grey trunk
It likes emerald tasty grass
It has huge, thin ears for hearing
It has a ginormous black body
It is a herbivore
because it eats grass and plants
What is it?

Answer: An elephant.

**Evie Davies (6)**
St George's Primary School, Church Gresley

# What Am I?

It has a tiny, bumpy tail
It lives in the dark, creepy wild
It is a mammal
It has a round, brown nose
It has rectangle, long legs
It has long, pointy antlers
It eats small animals
It has tall, oval ears
What is it?

Answer: A deer.

**Holly Forrest (7)**
St George's Primary School, Church Gresley

# Slithery

It eats juicy, tiny chameleons
It is a little, sparkly reptile
It is a scary, furious animal
It slithers like a snail
It finds a pile of logs to call home
It is scaly and rough
It has golden, scary eyes
What is it?

Answer: A snake.

**Emily Davis (7)**
St George's Primary School, Church Gresley

# Furry Animal

It has dark, black stripes
It is a fierce animal that hunts for prey
It has green, fearsome eyes
It has scary yellow teeth
It has giant claws
It's a dangerous creature
It runs as fast as a hurricane
What is it?

Answer: A tiger.

**George Elwyn Weighall (6)**
St George's Primary School, Church Gresley

# Slimy, Slithery

It has a ruby, red tongue
It has an emerald, scaly body
It can slither up black, brown trees
It lives in the jungle
It has a long, colourful body
It is poisonous
It eats insects
It has black eyes
What is it?

Answer: A snake.

**Olivia Sophia Cook (6)**
St George's Primary School, Church Gresley

# Long Slitherer

It lives in the jungle
It has a dangerous bite
It slithers slowly so it can hunt
It has a ruby, long tongue
It is a reptile
It is a carnivore because it eats meat
It is a spiral, emerald shape
What is it?

Answer: A snake.

**Phoebe Leah Felthouse (7)**
St George's Primary School, Church Gresley

# Slither

It slithers along the jungle
It eats delicious chameleons
It has no legs, so it slides around
It has long, yellow stripes
It can be eaten
It is scary and ferocious
It is like a snail
What is it?

Answer: A snake.

**Leila Miles (6)**
St George's Primary School, Church Gresley

# Spotty

It is tall
It has round, brown spots
It eats pointy, emerald leaves
It has a long, spotty neck
It lives in Africa
It has four small legs
It is friendly
It has lots of courage
What is it?

*Answer: A giraffe.*

**Maisie Bailey (6)**
St George's Primary School, Church Gresley

# Bony Plates

It can curl up in a ball
It is very small
It's not as quick as a cheetah
It's got a fluffy tummy
It is kind
It defends itself from predators
in a good way
What is it?

*Answer: An armadillo.*

**Jessica Morritt (6)**
St George's Primary School, Church Gresley

# Spotty

It has soft fur
It has lots of black spots
It has long, sharp claws
It has four spotty legs
It is very wild
It bites a lot
What is it?

Answer: A cheetah.

**Tallula Young (7)**
St George's Primary School, Church Gresley

# Hoppy

It has a short, fluffy tail
It has long ears
It hops around
It has whiskers
It lives in a hutch
It eats orange carrots
What is it?

*Answer: A rabbit.*

**Chloe Warrilow (7)**
St George's Primary School, Church Gresley

# Roary

It has long claws
It has four legs
It has a rough tongue
It has lots of fur
It hunts for prey
It has a black nose
What is it?

Answer: A lion cub.

**Skye Cuthbert (6)**
St George's Primary School, Church Gresley

# Slithery

It has a scaly skin
It has a long tail
It has a rough body
It has blue eyes
It has a red body
It has a sharp tail
What is it?

Answer: A snake.

**Chelsey Jerome (6)**
St George's Primary School, Church Gresley

# Snappy

It has a big tongue
It has terrifying teeth
It has scales
It has sharp teeth
It is green
It has dots
What is it?

Answer: A crocodile

**Oliver-Jack Grime (7)**
St George's Primary School, Church Gresley

# Furry

It has an orange body
It has a big furry mane
It hunts prey
It has sharp teeth
It is the king of the jungle
What is it?

*Answer: A lion.*

**Tianna Gutteridge (7)**
St George's Primary School, Church Gresley

# Furry

It has a furry body
It has big claws
It has four feet
It has pretty eyes
It is black and white
What is it?

Answer: A koala.

**Makayla Avah Foster (6)**
St George's Primary School, Church Gresley

# The Special Scraper

I sneak up on people, I can be a pet
I am furry, cuddly, lovely
and sometimes scary
I come in black, black and white and ginger
I can be mean, I have sharp teeth
I run quickly, I am as big as a dog
I have a fluffy tail
I am an animal, I hide in bushes
I jump in trees
I like playing with balls
I am sometimes scared
I run away from playing games
Some people think I am cute
I crawl around in the grass
Sometimes I go crazy
What am I?

Answer: A cat.

**Molly Marianne Rowan (6)**
Stanley St Andrew's CE Primary School, Stanley

# The Hopper

I have sharp teeth, I jump like a kangaroo
I love cuddles, I am fluffy and soft
I have floppy ears, I love to eat carrots
My tail is like a cloud
I come in lots of colours like brown,
white or black
I like to gnaw wood
I am fluffy like a teddy bear
I like eating thin, green grass
What am I?

Answer: A bunny.

**Elizabeth Knifton (7)**
Stanley St Andrew's CE Primary School, Stanley

# Silly Scratcher

My colours are black, white,
ginger and brown
I am very fluffy and soft
I have long naps in the sun
I scratch when I get angry
I love fish
I love to kill rats and birds
and walk in a nearby field
I am as cute as a button
I trot like a deer
What am I?

Answer: A cat.

**Amelia Lister (6)**
Stanley St Andrew's CE Primary School, Stanley

# The Fire Demon

I blow down big, brick houses
I creep through the big, dark woods
If you come to my lair you will die
I'm as hot as the sun
I don't come out in daylight
I stomp through the deep, dark wood
I roar as loud as a lion
What am I?

Answer: A dragon.

**Elliot Sullivan (7)**
Stanley St Andrew's CE Primary School, Stanley

# What Am I?

I only have feet the size of acorns
I have a small black nose
My spikes are big and black
Don't touch me without gloves
I am very spiky
I creep in your garden at night
I eat dog food and cat food
What am I?

Answer: A hedgehog.

**Oliver Crowder (6)**
Stanley St Andrew's CE Primary School, Stanley

# The Fluffy Horse

I have sparkly feet
I can be brown, pink or purple
I have a big, fluffy tail
Lots of people like me, especially children
People take pictures of me
I am not a pet but I live in a field
What am I?

Answer: A unicorn.

**Edie Kate Hughes (6)**
Stanley St Andrew's CE Primary School, Stanley

# The Chomper

I'm as hard as rock
I am very fierce
I can hurt you
I zoom across the dusty desert
I eat disgusting, slimy maggots
I might pinch you
with my sharp, dangerous claws
What am I?

Answer: A scorpion.

**George Izzard (7)**
Stanley St Andrew's CE Primary School, Stanley

# The Cutie

I scratch when I get angry
I can be scary but not always
I have paws
I am medium sized
I have a fluffy tail
I'm like a tiger
I climb trees
I have sharp teeth
What am I?

Answer: A cat.

**Lily Deley (6)**
Stanley St Andrew's CE Primary School, Stanley

# The Nut Eaters

I am as cuddly as my teddy
I eat small, brown nuts
I am endangered
I am red
I've got lots of species
I make no noise,
and I have teeth like a rabbit
What am I?

*Answer: A red squirrel.*

**Joseph Harry Smyth (7)**
Stanley St Andrew's CE Primary School, Stanley

# The Fluff Fluff

I am fluffy
I like taking walks
I love being cuddled
I can be a cocker spaniel or water spaniel
I can be a puppy or an adult
I have very sharp teeth and a tail
What am I?

Answer: A dog.

**Lochlan Campbell (6)**
Stanley St Andrew's CE Primary School, Stanley

# The Magic House

I have a beautiful, huge flag
I am as tall as a mountain
I am as shiny as a knight's armour
I am stiff and strong
I have a big, curved door
I am magical
What am I?

Answer: A castle.

**Aimee Dennis (7)**
Stanley St Andrew's CE Primary School, Stanley

# The Wing Flapper

I flap my amazing wings but I don't fly
I do my best to waddle
I make a big splash!
I'm as black as the night
I'm white too
I waddle on ice
What am I?

Answer: A penguin.

## Fearne Hilditch (7)

Stanley St Andrew's CE Primary School, Stanley

# Fire Flyer

I have dark, round eyes,
I am long and big
I have a tail
And I am like a flamethrower
I'm powerful and I'm strong
I roar as loud as a lion
What am I?

Answer: A dragon.

**Jack Stephenson (7)**
Stanley St Andrew's CE Primary School, Stanley

# What Am I?

I breathe fireballs
I flap my long, swishy tail
I can be red and orange
I can breathe fire
I can eat you
I can have spikes
I can drink water
What am I?

Answer: A dragon.

**Kayden Brent Hodson (7)**
Stanley St Andrew's CE Primary School, Stanley

# The Spotty Creature

I have antennas
I'm red and spotty
I'm as small as an ant
When I fly I go buzz
I can be yellow as well
I'm a small, tiny creature
What am I?

Answer: A ladybug.

**Olivia Bradley (6)**
Stanley St Andrew's CE Primary School, Stanley

# The Fire Demon

Out of my mouth comes burning flames
I will eat you
I am very, very scary
I roar very, very loud
I can burn marshmallows
I am very dry
What am I?

Answer: A dragon.

## Dalacey Peace (6)

Stanley St Andrew's CE Primary School, Stanley

# The Cold Thing

I am fluffy and snowy
I love to stand like a statue
I have stone eyes
I have a carrot nose
I have stick arms
Children love to make me
What am I?

Answer: A snowman.

**Logan Doughty (7)**
Stanley St Andrew's CE Primary School, Stanley

# The Fire Demon

I am a fire flyer
I fight in war
I throw fireballs
I have golden spots
I am in the Chinese parade
I have very, very, shiny claws
What am I?

Answer: A dragon.

**Imogen Izzard (7)**
Stanley St Andrew's CE Primary School, Stanley

# The Grass Jumper

I can zoom across grass easily
I can climb up trees
I am very long
I'm like lightning
I sniff the air
I have a long tongue
What am I?

Answer: A snake.

**Lucas Pierrepont (6)**
Stanley St Andrew's CE Primary School, Stanley

# What Am I?

I am orange and red
I am fluffy and soft
I run up trees
I run fast
I eat acorns and nuts
I am endangered
What am I?

Answer: A red squirrel.

**Olivia Grace Dennis (7)**
Stanley St Andrew's CE Primary School, Stanley

YoungWriters
Est.1991

# YOUNG WRITERS INFORMATION

We hope you have enjoyed reading this book – and that you will continue to in the coming years.

If you're a young writer who enjoys reading and creative writing, or the parent of an enthusiastic poet or story writer, do visit our website **www.youngwriters.co.uk**. Here you will find free competitions, workshops and games, as well as recommended reads, a poetry glossary and our blog.

If you would like to order further copies of this book, or any of our other titles, then please give us a call or visit **www.youngwriters.co.uk**.

Young Writers
Remus House
Coltsfoot Drive
Peterborough
PE2 9BF
(01733) 890066
info@youngwriters.co.uk